Marv
and the
Monarch
Butterflies

by Brian Krumm
illustrated by Cinzia Battistel

a Capstone company — publishers for children

Engage Literacy is published in the UK by Raintree.
Raintree is an imprint of Capstone Global Library Limited, a company
incorporated in England and Wales having its registered office at 264 Banbury
Road, Oxford, OX2 7DY – Registered company number: 6695582

www.raintree.co.uk

Printed and bound in China.

Marvin and the Monarch Butterflies

ISBN: 978 1 4747 1824 0

Contents

Chapter 1

Road trip

My name is Marvin, and Kayla is my best friend. We live in a small town in the United States. Kayla loves butterflies more than anyone. She talks about them all the time.

"Amazing!" she always says when she sees one in the sky. Then she points to it.

Kayla wanted me to go to a special butterfly tagging event. It would be a long car journey away. She's been going to this event for years.

At the event, people put tiny stickers called "tags" on the wings of monarch butterflies. Then they let the butterflies fly away. The stickers help people to learn about the butterflies. When people find a butterfly with a sticker, they can e-mail or call to report finding it. Scientists use this information to find out more about how far these butterflies migrate, or travel to another location.

I was more interested in playing my guitar, but I decided to go. It would be a good trip, and it would mean the world to Kayla if I went.

"Marvin, they're here," my mum yelled from the kitchen. I looked out of the window and saw Kayla's family car pull up.

"Are you ready for a magical butterfly experience?" asked Kayla, as I walked up to the car.

"I can't wait. Although I'm sure we'll be talking about butterflies the whole way there," I laughed.

I loaded my guitar and a stuffed red rucksack into the car. Kayla's dad winked at me.

"You're not the only one who Kayla talks to about butterflies," her dad said. "I never thought I would know as much about butterflies as I do now!"

Like Kayla, my grandma had always loved butterflies. Her entire house was covered with butterfly decorations. She had them in the bathroom, her bedroom, the kitchen and the living room. Her house attracted a lot of butterflies, so this trip reminded me of her.

"OK. Load up! The Butterfly Car is about to depart," Kayla's dad smiled. "It's a long drive to the butterfly tagging, so let's get going."

The butterfly tagging takes place near a university. Most of the people who go to the event are from nearby. We would probably be the only ones who travelled from far away.

I waved to my mum from the car window as we pulled out of our street.

Chapter 2
On the road

Kayla was more than ready for the long trip. She had her laptop along for the ride and several books on monarch butterflies.

"Isn't it amazing?" said Kayla. She started rattling off butterfly facts. "Just think. Some monarchs could be taking the same trip as us, on their way to the country of Mexico. Millions of them, maybe even a billion, make the trip from Canada every autumn. They fly right over the United States. Some of them travel thousands of kilometres to get to Mexico."

"Wow," I said. "How do we know they make the trip every year?"

"One way we know is because we can see pictures of them in Mexico," said Kayla. "They fly to the same forests every year, and they arrive in mid-October. This is interesting, listen! Some people believe that the butterflies are human spirits returning to Earth."

Kayla showed me a picture on her laptop of the butterflies in a lush, green forest.

"That's so cool," I said. "It looks like the entire forest turns orange that time of year."

"I know," replied Kayla. "Did you know that the weight of the butterflies can bend branches of the trees in the forests? Sometimes the branches even break!"

"I would love to see the butterflies in Mexico sometime," I said.

"Let's promise each other, that when we're older, we'll go to Mexico together to see the butterflies," said Kayla.

"I promise, as long as I can bring my guitar," I laughed. "How else do we know that the butterflies make this trip?"

"That's the reason we're going to the butterfly event," said Kayla. "Our plan is to tag and release butterflies. People all over the United States and in Mexico find the butterflies with tags on them. I'll tell you all about it at Aunt Ruth's house."

Kayla's dad said, "I hope you don't mind if we stop to visit my younger sister, who lives along the way. I think you'll like her. She plays guitar, too."

"That sounds great. It will be nice to be able to play guitar with someone," I said. "And after four hours in a car, I'll be ready for a break."

Chapter 3
A dream at Aunt Ruth's

Aunt Ruth was waiting outside the block of flats for us.

"Hello brother," said Ruth. "It's great to see you! And I'm so glad that you brought my beautiful butterfly princess!"

"Hi Aunt Ruth," Kayla said as she smiled and hugged her aunt. "This is my friend Marvin."

"So you play guitar, too?" asked Ruth.

"I sure do," I said. "But now I'm more like a guitar-playing butterfly expert."

"Don't tease!" said Kayla. "You know I just love talking about butterflies."

That night we stayed at Aunt Ruth's house. Aunt Ruth was great. She got out her guitar after dinner and said she wanted to play a song for us. I took out my guitar, too. The song was called "Flying Down to Mexico."

"Here's how it goes, Marvin," she said and showed me the chords. Then she started to sing:

Before the winter starts to freeze.
Before the children begin to sneeze.
I'm going to fly high. I'm going to fly low.
I'm going to fly down to Mexico.

It turns out that Kayla learned about butterflies from Ruth. Ruth's house looked a lot like my grandma's house. There were butterfly decorations everywhere. I even saw a butterfly on the window.

Ruth also told us about the times she had been butterfly tagging.

"One year," said Ruth, "I was able to tag 50 butterflies! That is a lot!"

That night, we slept on the soft carpet in sleeping bags. Kayla kept talking about butterflies as everybody was trying to sleep. She was telling us how many kilometres they need to fly each day. She was still talking about what the butterflies go through on their trip when I finally closed my eyes.

I drifted off to sleep and had a dream that I was a migrating butterfly. I was flying over a huge lake. I had been flying for hours, and I couldn't go any further. Luckily, I saw a fishing boat on the lake. I landed on the ship's deck and rested on a coil of rope.

I had just taken off into the air again when I woke up. I had to look around me to remember where I was.

As soon as I awoke, I remembered what Kayla had told me. Flying over huge lakes is a difficult part of the journey for monarchs. It can be dangerous. They also have to fly many kilometres each day to get to Mexico by October.

"Wow! I just dreamed I was a butterfly flying over a huge lake. It was like I was really there," I whispered to Kayla.

"Imagine what it must be like to fly thousands of kilometres in a few months," said Kayla. "You would be very, very tired!"

Chapter 4
To the butterfly tagging

16

After breakfast, we said goodbye to Aunt Ruth and drove off in the direction of the butterfly tagging. Kayla found more information about the tags we would put on the butterflies.

"It's amazing!" said Kayla. "This website says that over the years, hundreds of thousands of monarchs have stopped in the place where we are going. The butterflies like to stop for the nectar, which is a sweet liquid found in many of the yellow flowers that grow there."

As we drove on, I began to see fields of yellow flowers everywhere. I saw orange butterflies flying above the flowers. I was getting excited to see the butterflies up close.

As Kayla and her dad were chatting about the event, I imagined myself as the monarch butterfly I had dreamed about. I stared out of the window and thought about what it would be like to stop in the fields after a long journey.

Kayla's dad stopped the car so that we could stretch our legs. Kayla showed me a website on her laptop.

The website showed a diagram of the tags that are used to track the butterflies. The tags, which are lightweight and waterproof, stick on the butterfly wings. The butterflies can fly just fine with the stickers.

"Believe it or not, hundreds of tagged butterflies are found each year," Kayla said. "There's a number on each tag, a phone number and an e-mail address to use to contact the butterfly group. A lot of the tagged butterflies are found dead. But even those butterflies can help us understand the routes that butterflies take to travel to Mexico," said Kayla.

She went on to explain. "Scientists can also tell how long the migration took and what the weather was like along the way. There are people along the migration route who look for the butterflies. It's especially helpful if people find the butterflies in Mexico."

"I guess those butterflies can tell us how long the migration took, so they are the most important to find," Kayla's dad suggested.

"They give us the most valuable information, for sure," Kayla agreed. "They let us know that they were able to make the journey."

Chapter 5
How to tag a butterfly

We pulled off of the main road towards where the event was being held. As we drove into the car park, I noticed a group of kids had already begun tagging butterflies. Volunteers were showing them how to do it.

"Hi, I'm Chris!" a volunteer called to us. He looked at our dirty and dusty car. "Have you been travelling a while to get here?"

"We have," said Kayla. "We travelled for two days, and we're really excited to be here."

"Wow! You've come a long way. That deserves a special tagging lesson," said Chris.

Chris showed us a group of butterflies that were resting on some flowers. He was carrying a butterfly net.

"It's best to catch butterflies when they are feeding on flowers, rather than flying through the air," said Chris. "They'll keep flying away if you try to catch them in the air."

Chris handed me a butterfly net and showed me how to catch and hold a butterfly.

"First, make the net flat after you have a butterfly in the net," Chris explained. "Then, make sure the wings are closed over the butterfly's back. Gently hold the edge of the wings from the outside of the net. It's important to be very gentle. Next, hold the butterfly on the inside of the net by the middle part of its body. Slowly remove the butterfly from the net for tagging. Finally, apply the tag and release!"

Just like that, I was tagging butterflies! Kayla took a turn next. Chris gave us sheets to record our tag numbers and other information.

"So," I asked Chris, "why is it important to tag and track monarchs?"

"When we see butterflies all over the world," said Chris, "we know they are helping plants and animals. Butterflies help new plants to grow. They also provide food for other animals, such as birds."

"I've been trying to tell you these things for years. When we tag the butterflies, we are helping scientists study our natural world," said Kayla.

"That's really cool! Now I understand why you like this event so much, Kayla," I smiled. "I'm learning so much."

"Perhaps you'll be a real scientist, too, one day," Kayla's dad said to her.

With Chris's help, we tagged about 20 butterflies. We recorded the tag information on the sheets that Chris gave us. The sheets had the numbers from the stickers we put on the butterflies. We also wrote down the date that we tagged each butterfly. With each butterfly we released, Kayla did a little butterfly dance and said, "amazing."

Kayla's dad smiled and did the dance with his daughter.

I decided this would be a good time to play the song that Aunt Ruth taught me. Kayla's dad and I got my guitar from the car. As we watched some monarchs fly away, I began to sing:

Before the winter starts to freeze.
Before the children begin to sneeze.
I'm going to fly high. I'm going to fly low.
I'm going to fly down to Mexico.

Chapter 6
Back home

A few months later, I was back at home, lying in my cosy bed at night. The window of my bedroom was open, and I could feel a breeze blowing in.

Before I knew it, I was fast asleep and dreaming. I dreamed again that I was a monarch butterfly. I had finally arrived in Mexico. Millions of other monarchs were there, too. So many monarchs had been here before me. Millions more would come in the future.

I sat on a tree branch with hundreds of other butterflies. I felt the branch bend beneath our weight.

I woke up the next morning to the sound of knocking on my family's front door. It was Kayla. I looked out of my bedroom window. She was holding a messy stack of papers. I thought the papers were probably from the butterfly group.

"Come up," I shouted to Kayla from my open window.

My mum let Kayla in, and I could hear her run up the stairs to my bedroom. I quickly opened the door.

"We did it! One of our butterflies is in Mexico," shouted Kayla.

"That's fabulous!" I said.

"The sad news is that most of them didn't make it," said Kayla. "Some of our tags were found on dead butterflies along the way."

"Oh, no! That's a shame," I said.

"But a worker actually found one of our tags in Mexico on a live butterfly," said Kayla. "He e-mailed the information to the butterfly group. Can you believe it? One of our monarchs actually made it thousands of kilometres to Mexico!"

"I can believe it," I said. "Maybe it was the butterfly that I dreamed about last night. Maybe the butterfly actually made it all the way to Mexico."

"Or maybe it was a butterfly that heard you playing the butterfly song. Maybe you inspired it to make the journey," said Kayla. "That would be amazing, Marvin!"

I could feel a song coming on and reached for my guitar. But before I could start singing, Kayla interrupted me.

"Remember what you promised, Marvin," said Kayla. "When we get older, let's travel to Mexico with our families to see the butterflies."

"It's a deal," I smiled. "Sign me up, as long as I can take my guitar."